Scribbles and Ink

the

CONTEST

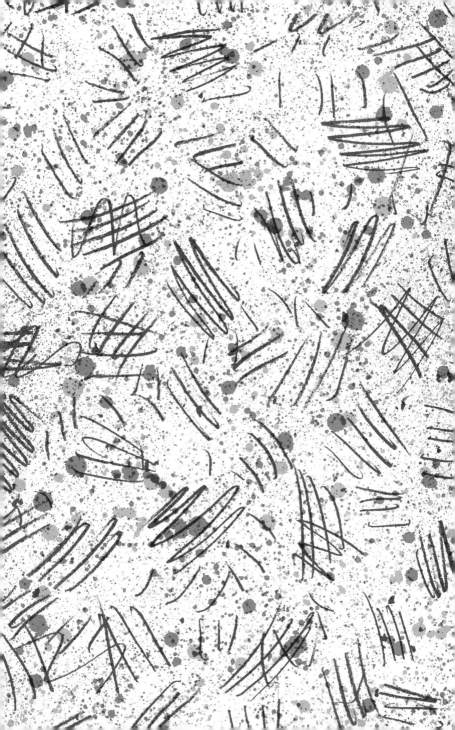

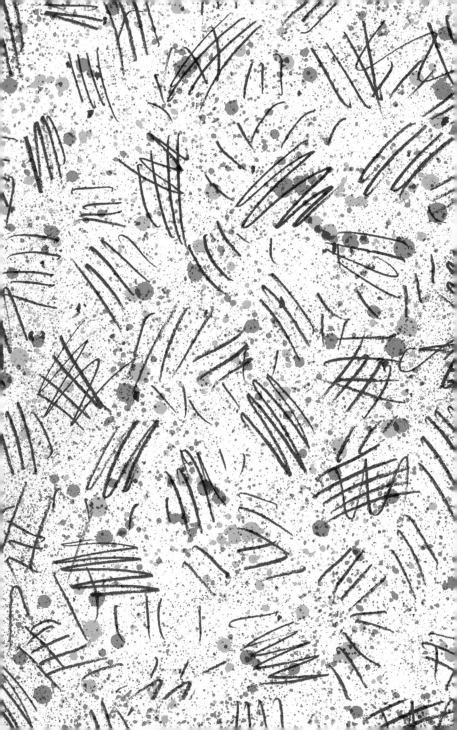

ISBN 978-0-545-83523-7

12 11 10 9 8 7 6 5 4 3 2 1   15 16 17 18 19 20/0

Printed in the U.S.A.   40

First Scholastic printing, February 2015

Scribbles and Ink

the CONTEST

by
ETHAN LONG

SCHOLASTIC INC.

Chapter 1
THE CONTEST

SCRIBBLES,
LOOK AT THIS!

DRAW A DINO!
WIN A PRIZE!

Show all your friends how **GREAT** you are!

FIRST PRIZE is a fabulous trip to

MUDSPLASH
MOUNTAIN

The **MUDDIEST** place on earth!

DEADLINE: tomorrow.

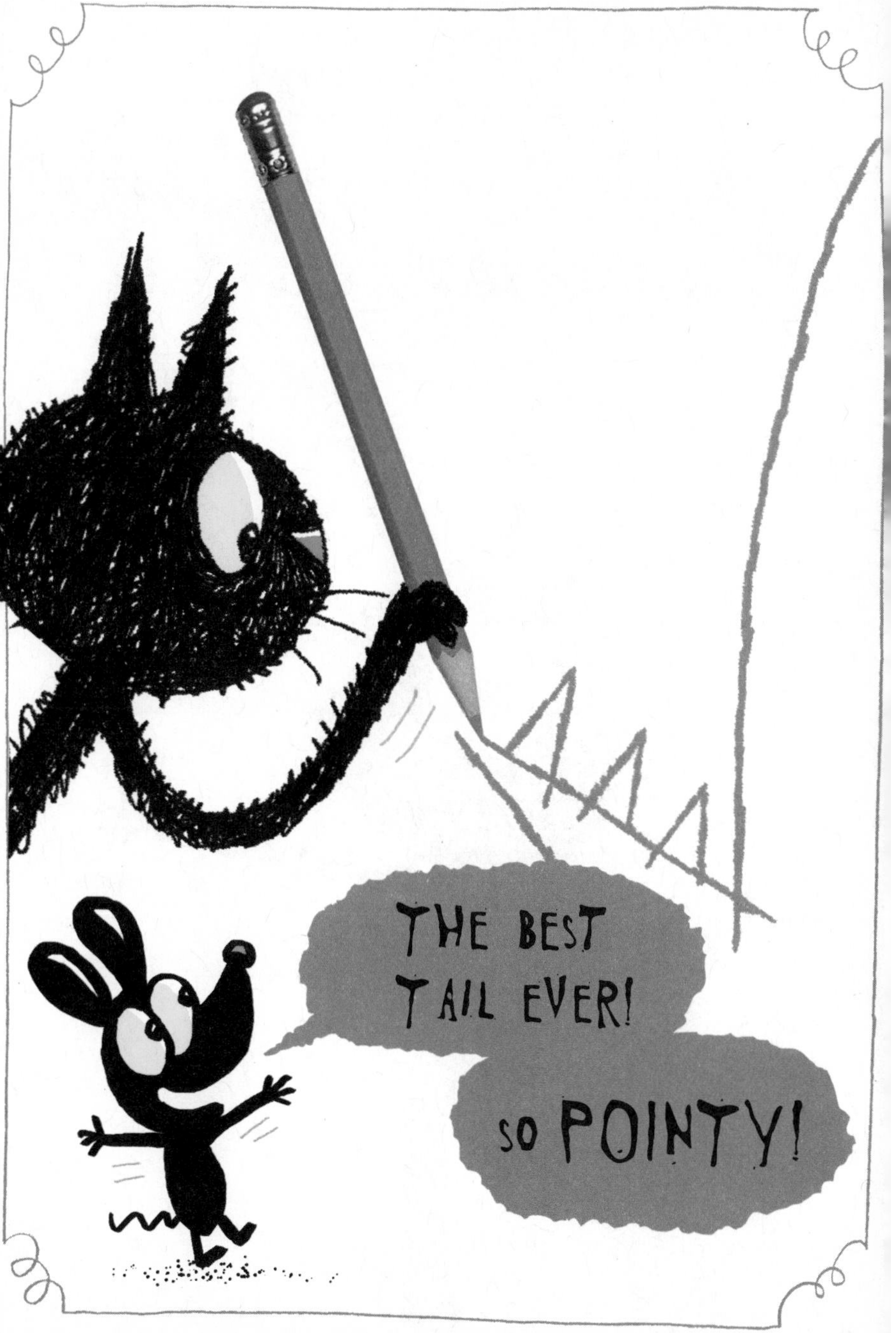
THE BEST TAIL EVER!
SO POINTY!

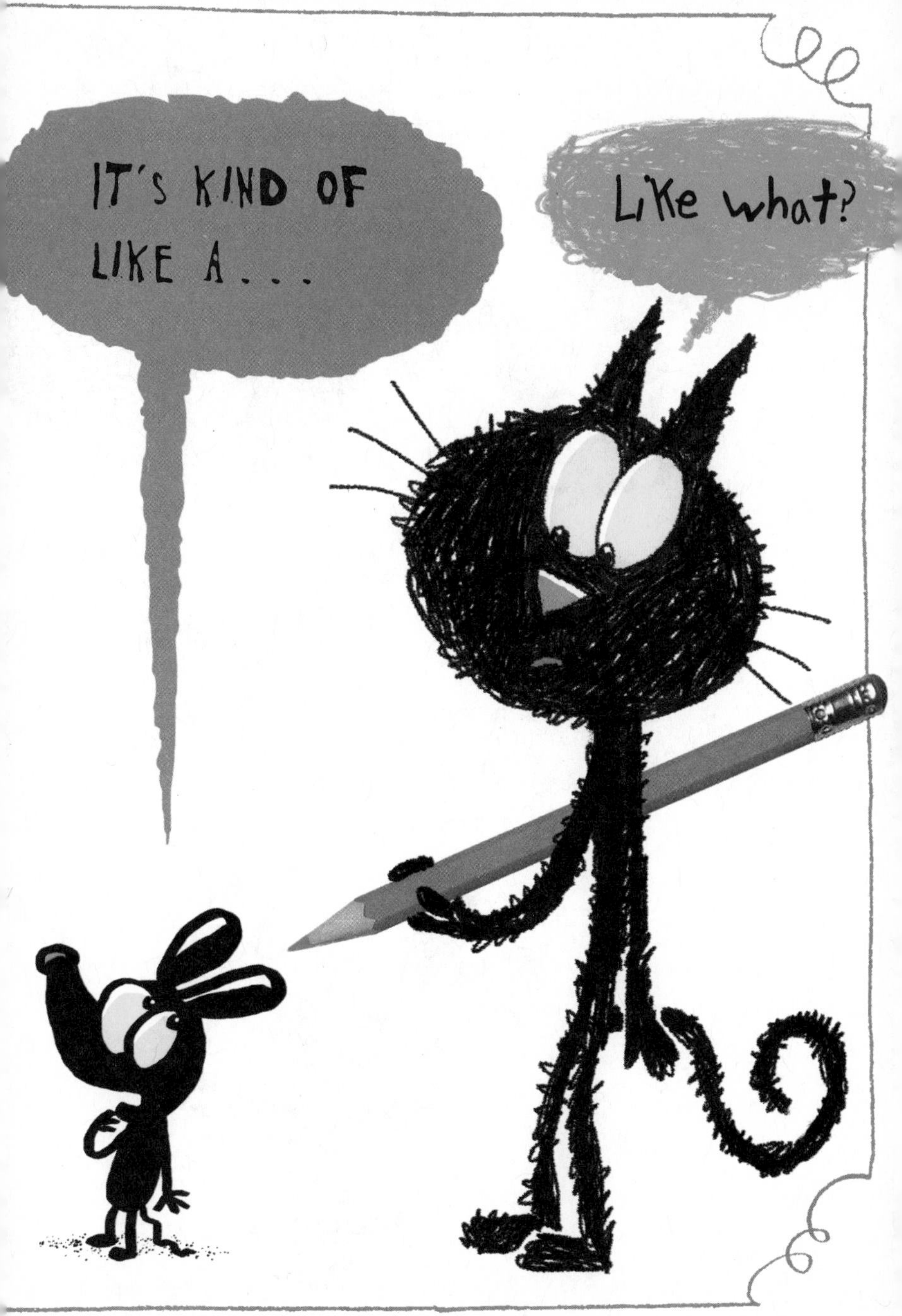
IT'S KIND OF LIKE A . . .
Like what?

IT'S A CHICK-A-SAURUS!

It is?

BEHOLD ITS BONY THIGHS AND FEATHERY BODY!

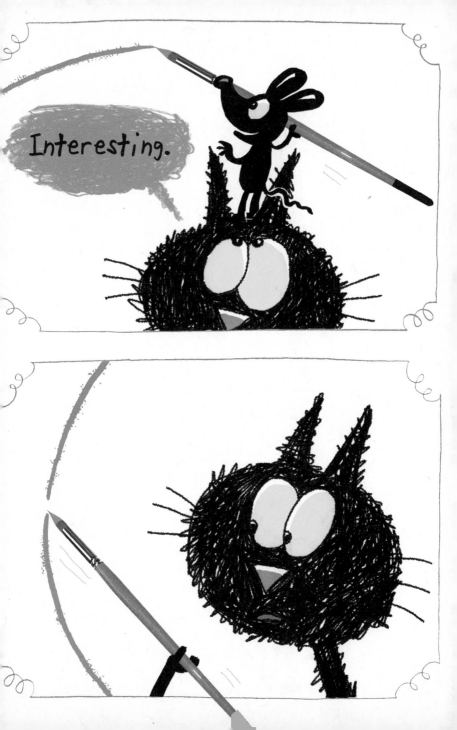

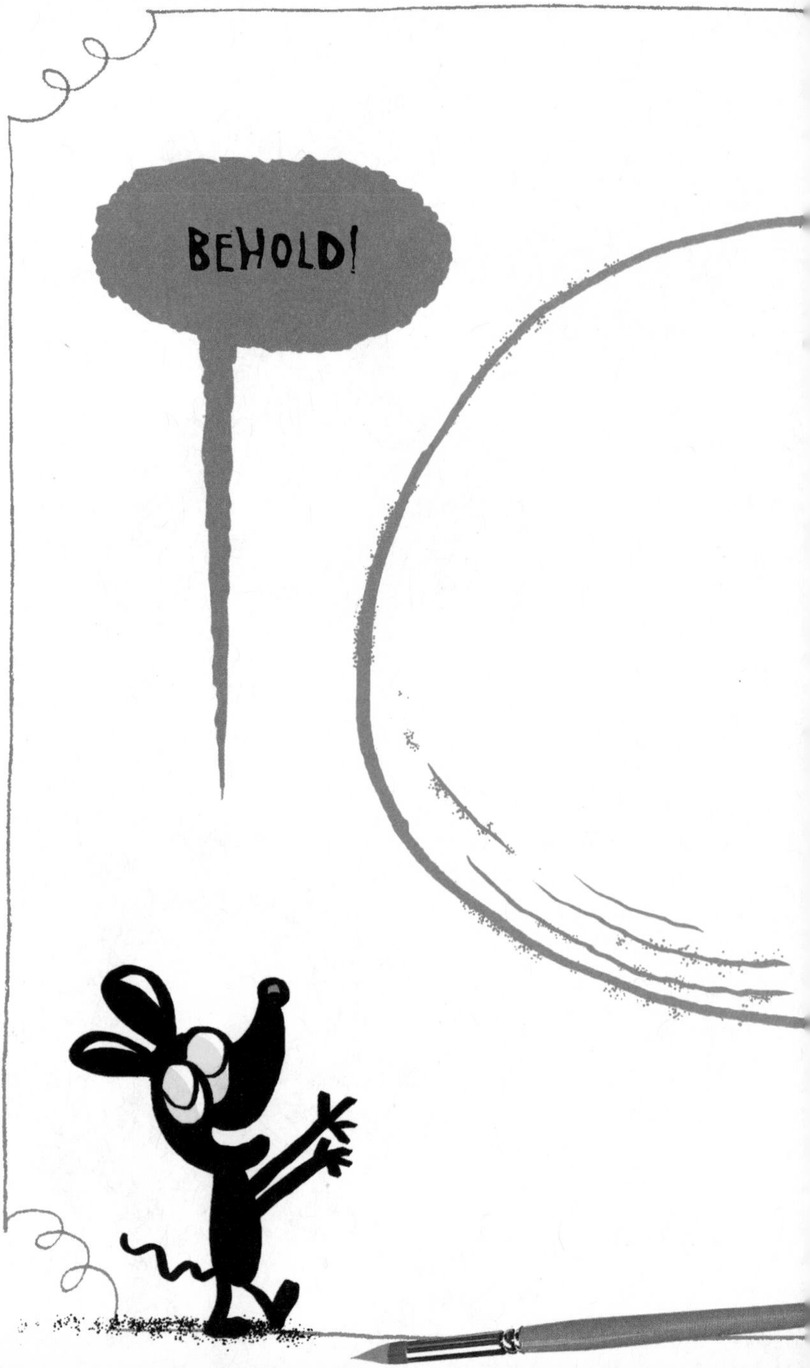
BEHOLD!

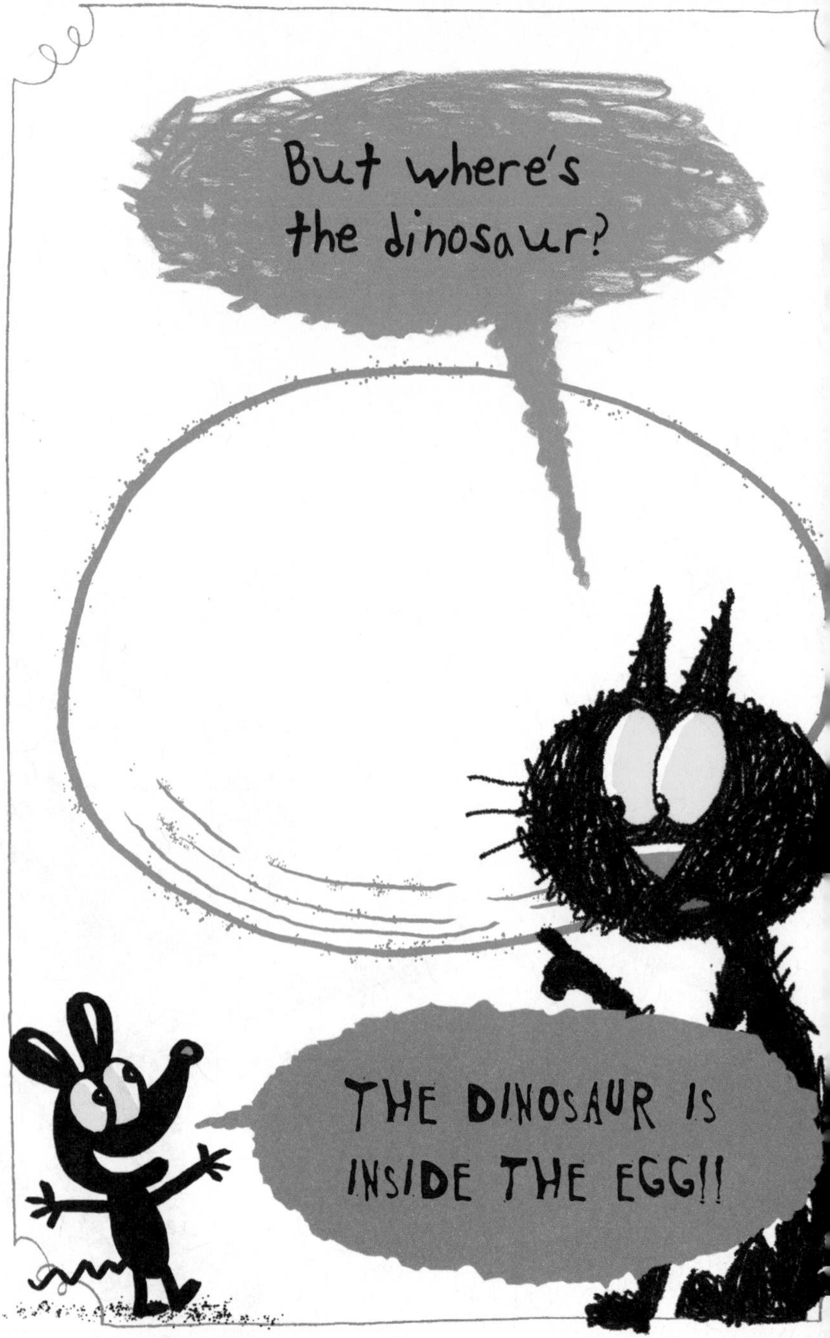
But where's the dinosaur?
THE DINOSAUR IS INSIDE THE EGG!!

EGG-SPLAIN THIS!

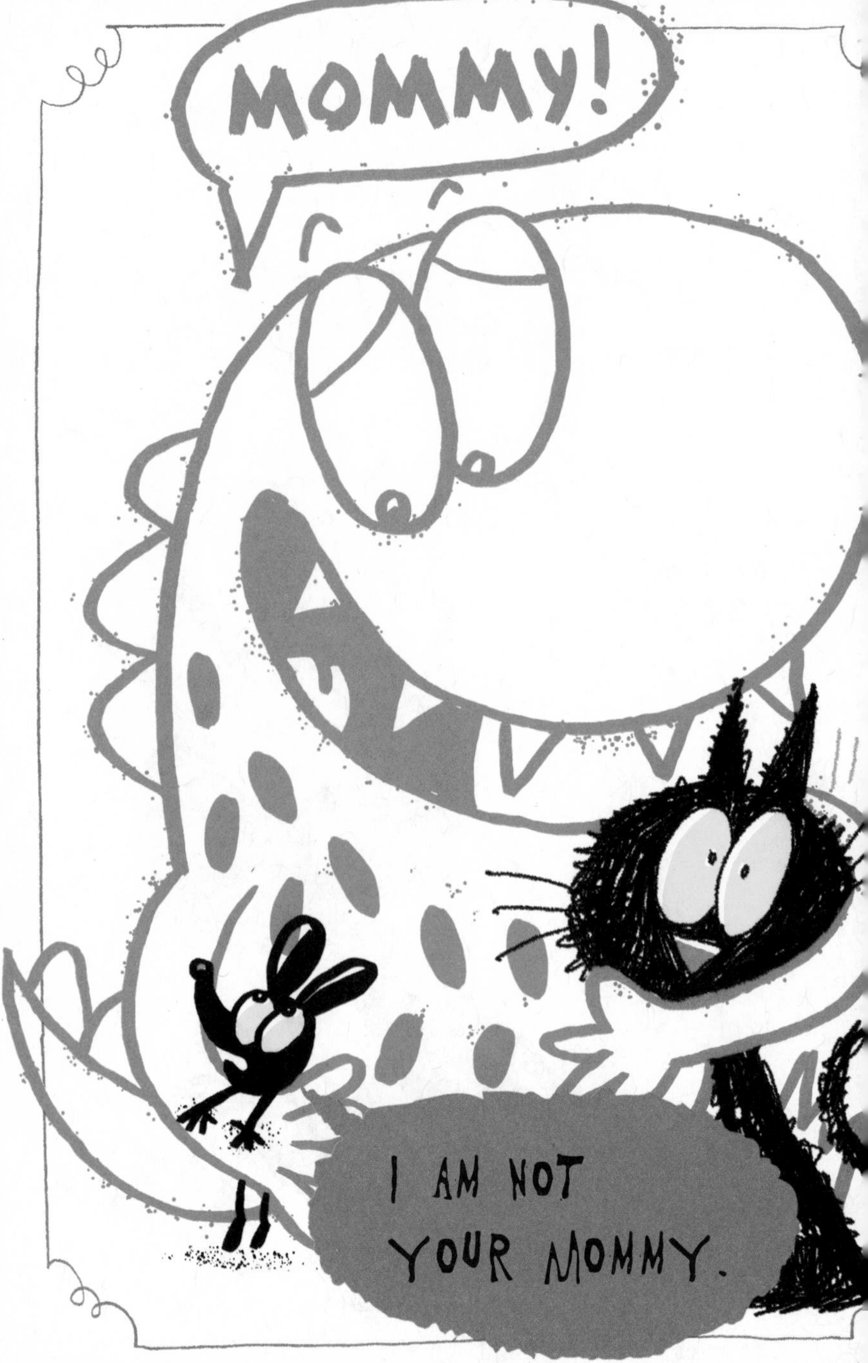
MOMMY!
I AM NOT YOUR MOMMY.

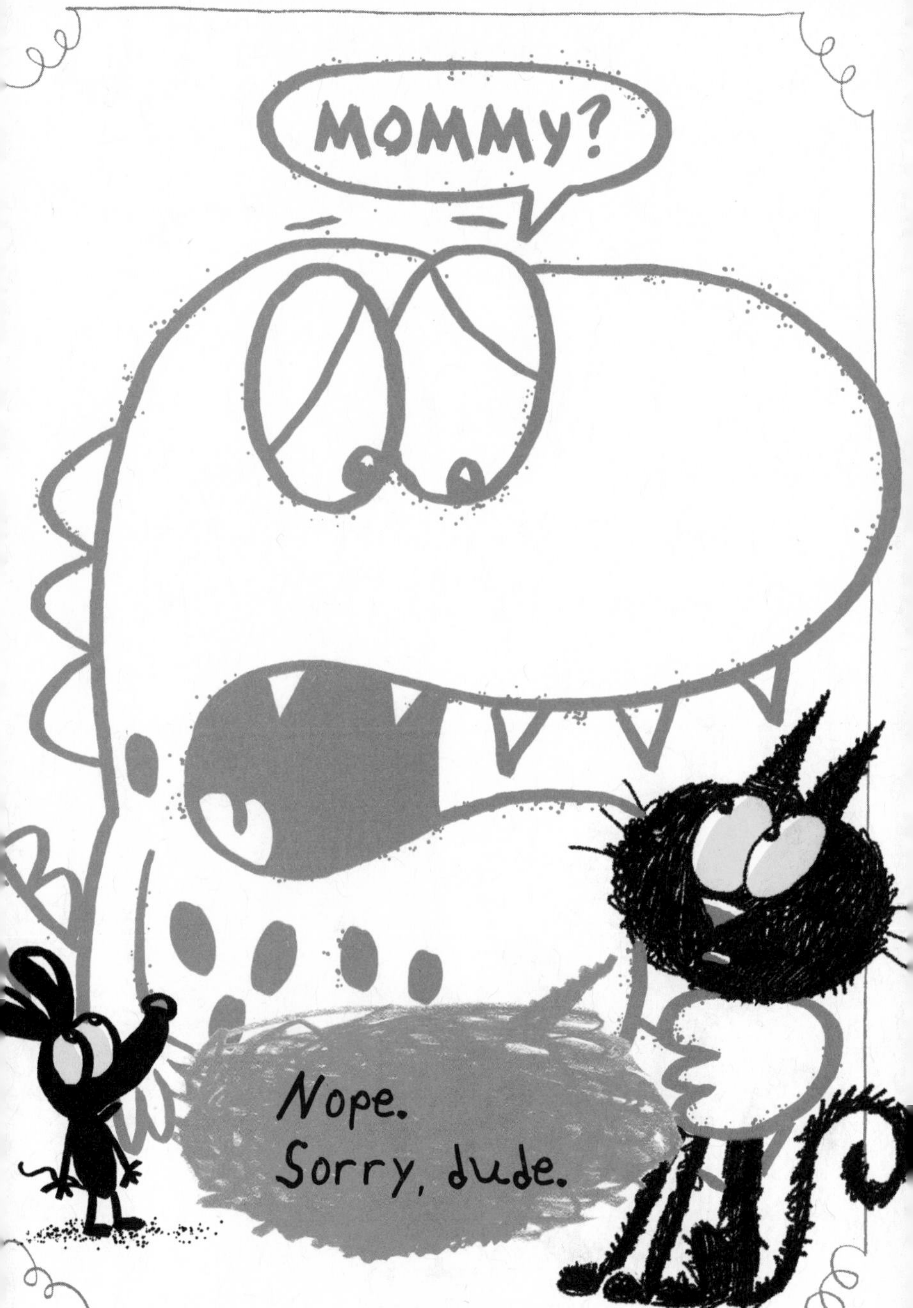
MOMMY?
Nope.
Sorry, dude.

Chapter 5
BEST EVER?

Good-bye, Chick-a-saurus!

SO LONG, BOO-BOO BABY

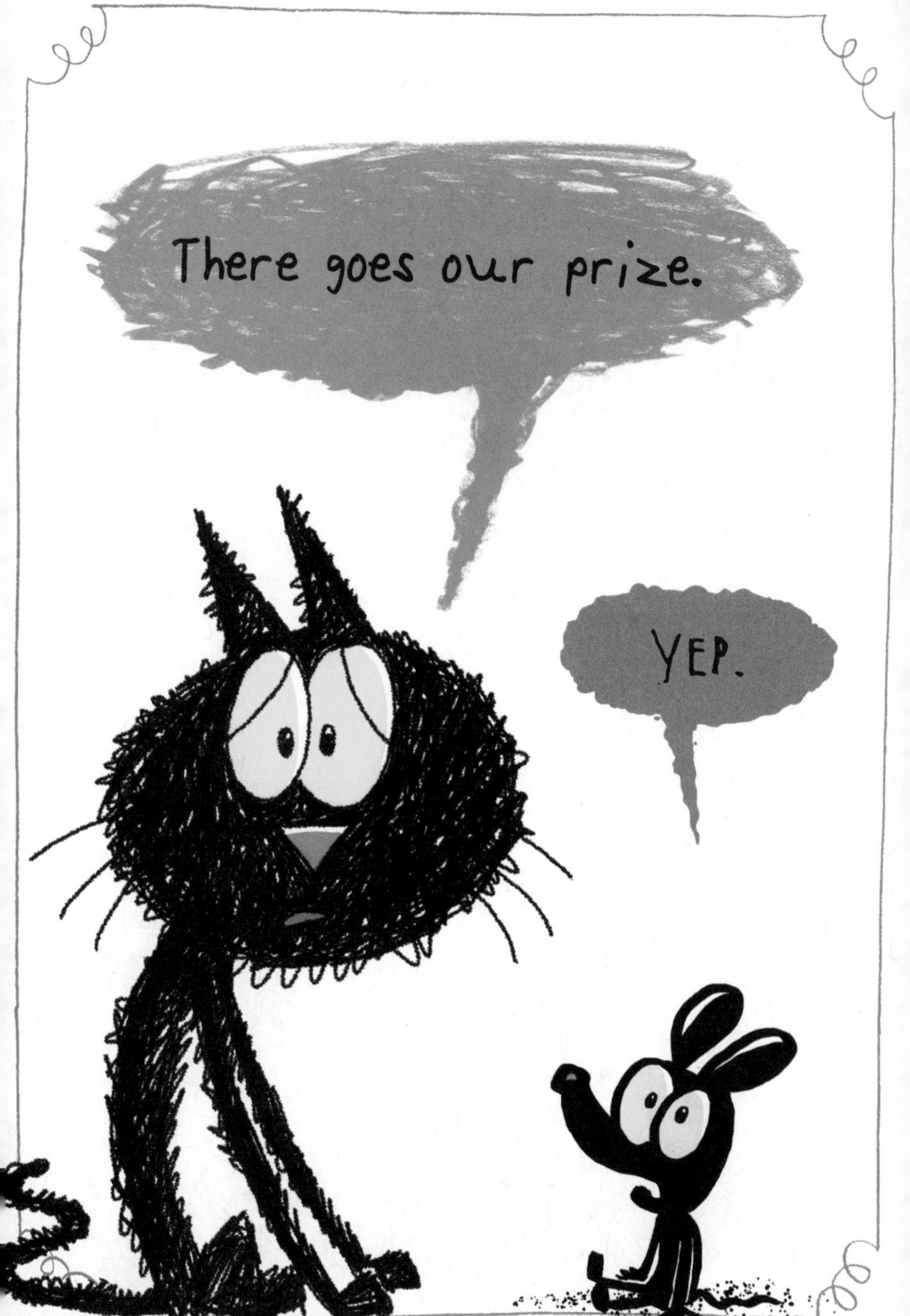
There goes our prize.
YEP.

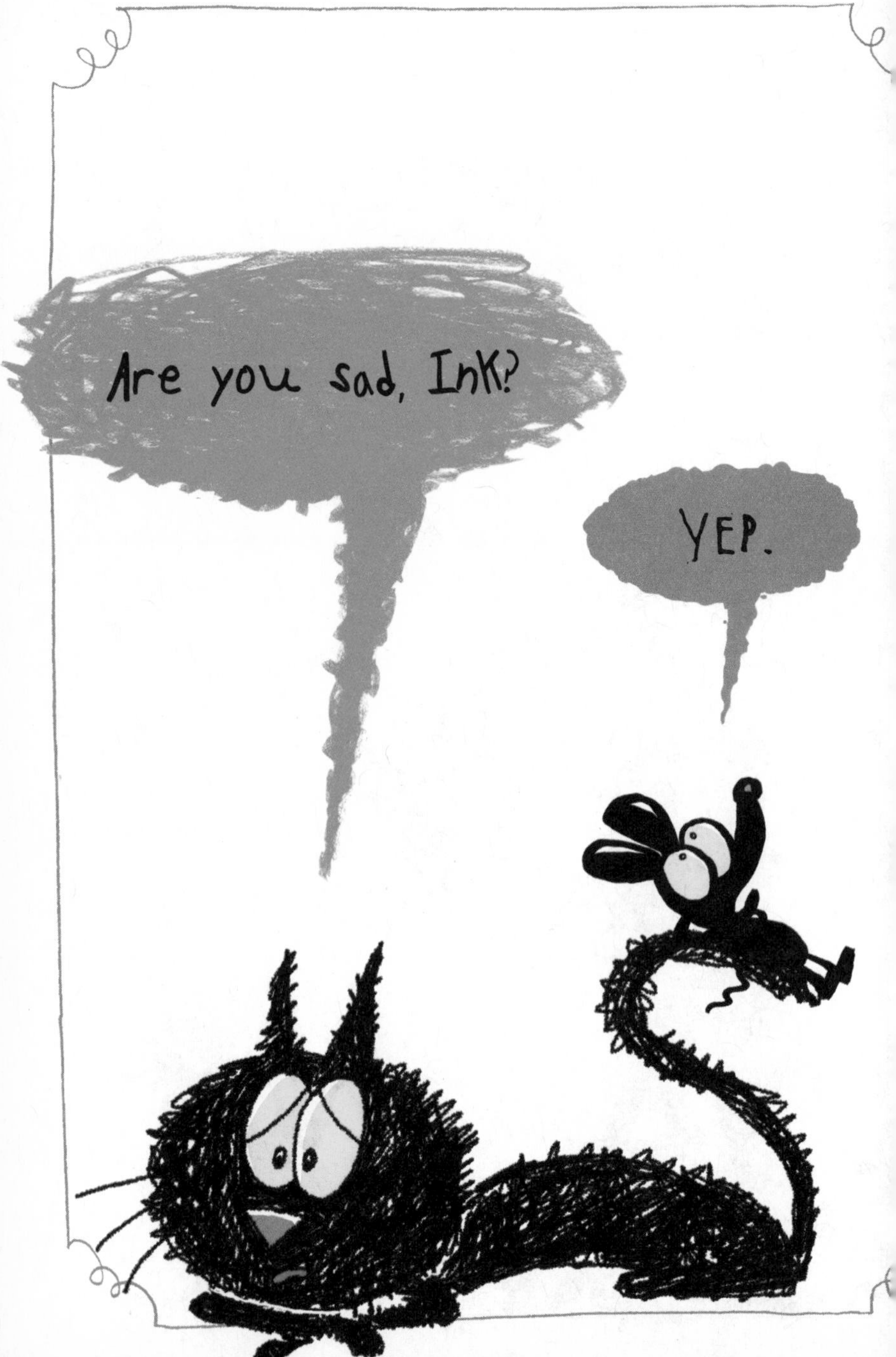
Are you sad, Ink?
YEP.

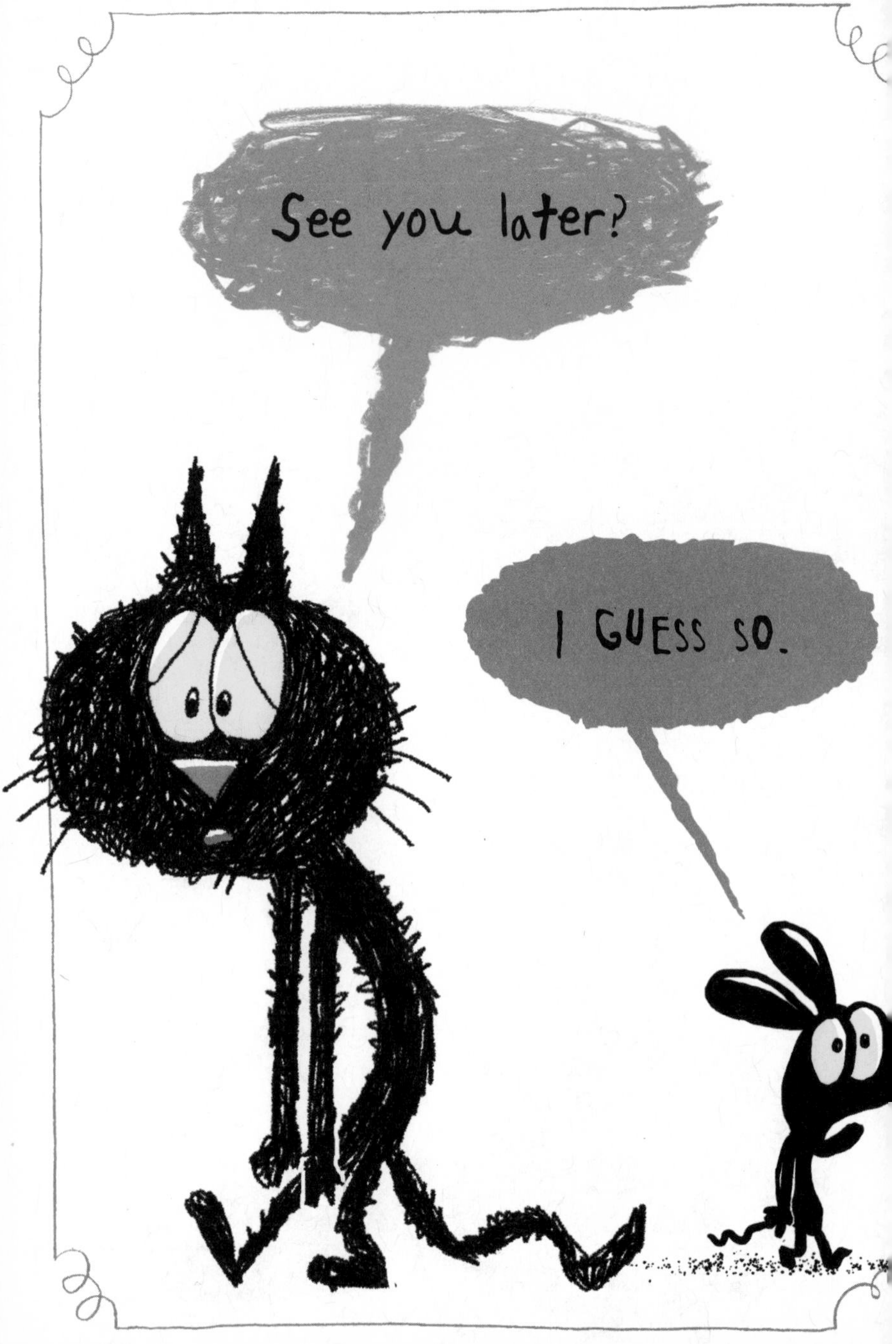
See you later?
I GUESS SO.

HEY, SCRIBBLES, COME HERE!
I HAVE SOMETHING FOR YOU.

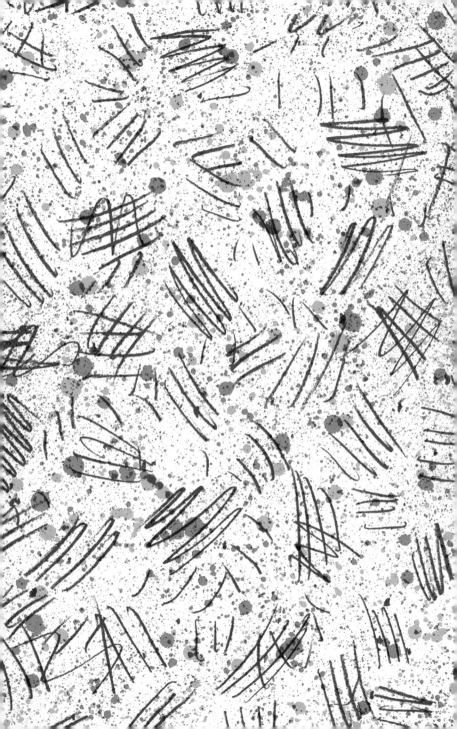

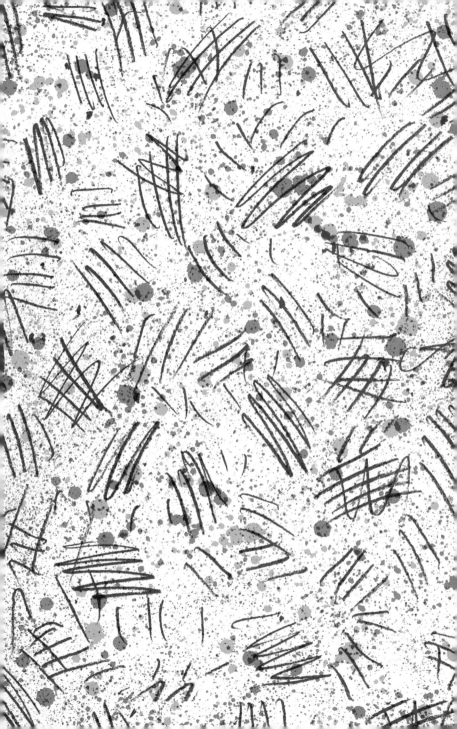

DRAWN TOGETHER AGAIN FOR MORE ARTISTIC SHENANIGANS!

Ink has discovered a contest with the greatest prize EVER!

Can these artist buddies draw the best dinosaur and win a trip to Mudsplash Mountain, the Muddiest Place on Earth?!

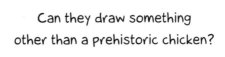

Can they draw something other than a prehistoric chicken?

Sharpen your pencils and dip your paints into this new artful adventure with Scribbles & Ink!

SCHOLASTIC

www.scholastic.com

ISBN 978-0-545-83523-7

EAN

9 780545 835237

Though the question is quite simple,
Simple answers might be wrong.
If you want to know the right one,
Help the genius all day long.
Morning, noon, and afternoon,
Till the night bird sings its song.

T his is the message that Jack and Annie of Frog Creek, Pennsylvania, get from Morgan le Fay, the magical librarian of Camelot. They know they have to search for one of the four secrets of happiness to help Merlin the magician find joy in his life again. And so they head off in the magic tree house for Florence, Italy, in the early 1500s to spend the day with one of the greatest artists and inventors of all time—Leonardo da Vinci!

Mary Pope Osborne takes young readers back to the time of the Renaissance, an amazing period when great art and new ideas flourished in Europe and helped change the world.

■ SCHOLASTIC
www.scholastic.com

ISBN-13: 978-0-545-14982-5
ISBN-10: 0-545-14982-0

EAN

9 780545 149825